718.00
0000

HEINEMANN ELT GUIDED READERS

ELEMENTARY LEVEL

The Lord of Obama's Messenger and Other Stories

A collection of tales from Japan

D1365021

CONFEDERATION COLLEGE
CHALLIS RESOURCE CENTRE

HEINEMANN ELT

ELEMENTARY LEVEL

Series Editor: John Milne

The Heinemann Elt Guided Readers provide a choice of enjoyable reading material for learners of English. The series is published at five levels – Starter, Beginner, Elementary, Intermediate and Upper. At **Elementary Level**, the control of content and language has the following main features:

Information Control
Stories have straightforward plots and a restricted number of main characters. Information which is vital to the understanding of the story is clearly presented and repeated when necessary. Difficult allusion and metaphor are avoided and cultural backgrounds are made explicit.

Structure Control
Students will meet those grammatical features which they have already been taught in their elementary course of studies. Other grammatical features occasionally occur with which the students may not be so familiar, but their use is made clear through context and reinforcement. This ensures that the reading as well as being enjoyable provides a continual learning situation for the students. Sentences are kept short – a maximum of two clauses in nearly all cases – and within sentences there is a balanced use of simple adverbial and adjectival phrases. Great care is taken with pronoun reference.

Vocabulary Control
At **Elementary Level** there is a limited use of a carefully controlled vocabulary of approximately 1,100 basic words. At the same time, students are given some opportunity to meet new or unfamiliar words in contexts where their meaning is obvious. The meaning of words introduced in this way is reinforced by repetition. Help is also given to the students in the form of vivid illustrations which are closely related to the text.

Contents

A Note About These Stories

There are four large islands in Japan – Hokkaido, Honshu, Shikoku and Kyushu. And there are many small islands.

For fourteen hundred years, emperors were the leaders of Japan. The Emperor of Japan was a god and he was the most important man in the land. He lived in the most important city – the capital city. After 1600, the capital city was Edo. Edo is now called Tokyo.

But the emperor did not rule Japan. Japan was divided into territories. Powerful families ruled each territory. Each territory was ruled by the lord of a family. These powerful lords were rich and they had armies of soldiers. Some of these fighting men were called *samurai*. Samurai were the best fighters in Japan. The strongest ruler of the most powerful territory was the ruler of all of Japan.

The people who lived in a territory respected their lord. The lord was right about all things. His people were polite. They did what the lord asked. It was their duty to do everything immediately. If someone did not do something, that person failed in his duty. Then that person would get no respect and he was disgraced. Every lord had to do duty to the most powerful lord. And everyone had to do duty to the emperor.

There are two main religions in Japan, Shinto and Buddhism. Shinto is the oldest Japanese religion. This religion began in Japan. People who believe in Shinto respect all human life. They also respect nature and the spirits that are in animals, trees and rocks. They believe in gods who take care of towns and villages.

In the sixth century, the religion of Buddhism came to Japan. Buddhism began in India. Buddhist monks are often in many old Japanese stories. Some of these monks lived in temples – places where people pray to the gods. Other monks travelled through the country. They told people about the words of Buddha.

Many old Japanese stories are about strange things that happen. Some stories are about spirits. Spirits are dead people who are not at peace. The spirits can change their bodies. Wicked spirits – goblins – try to kill people. Spells make people do strange and dangerous things.

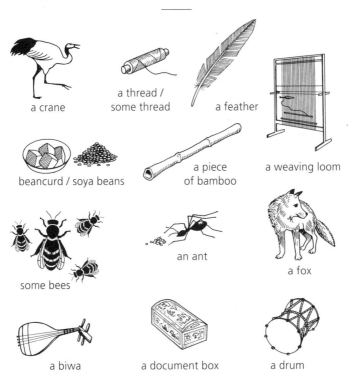

a crane

a thread / some thread

a feather

a weaving loom

beancurd / soya beans

a piece of bamboo

some bees

an ant

a fox

a biwa

a document box

a drum

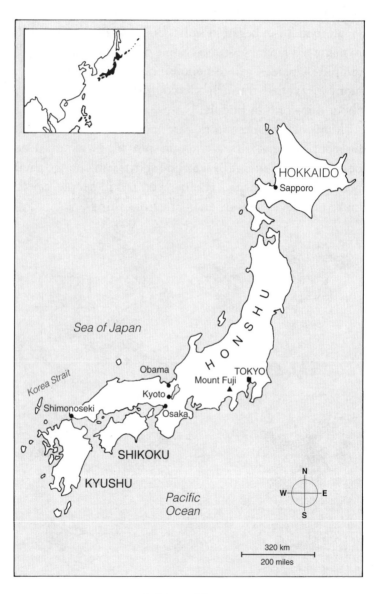

A Map of Japan

THE LORD OF OBAMA'S MESSENGER

Obama is a town on the coast of Japan. It is on the north coast of Honshu Island. Obama is a busy seaport and many ships sail to and from the port.

A long time ago, Obama was ruled by a wise lord. He loved people and he loved animals. He was always kind to the people of Obama and he never hurt animals. He was a good man. When he was the Lord of Obama, the people of Obama were happy.

One day, the lord was walking in the streets of Obama. He walked to the market. There were many shops which sold food and clothes. And there were many people buying things and selling things.

The lord walked slowly through the market. He held a walking stick in his hand. Sometimes he stopped and looked all around him. He looked at his people.

Suddenly, the Lord of Obama heard a lot of noise. Behind him, people were shouting and running. The lord saw some men carrying large sticks. The angry men were chasing a very beautiful, young red fox. They were trying to hit the fox.

The fox was running very fast and the men could not catch it. But one of the men had a big dog. The dog was running faster than the fox.

When the dog ran past him, the lord hit it with his walking stick. He did not want to hurt the dog. But he did not want the dog to catch the fox.

The dog howled and it stopped running. The fox escaped.

The lord spoke to the man who owned the dog.

'Why were you chasing that fox?' he asked.

'Sir, the fox stole some food from my shop,' the man replied. 'And it knocked over my table. The food fell onto the ground. I cannot sell that food now.'

'The fox is very hungry,' said the lord. 'Foxes do not often go into shops. They are afraid of people and they do not go near them.'

When the dog ran past him, the lord hit it with his walking stick.

The kind lord was sorry for the shopkeeper. But he did not want anybody to hurt the beautiful fox. He gave the shopkeeper some money.

'Take this money,' the lord said. 'It is payment for the food which fell onto the ground. But you must not chase the fox or hurt it.'

'I won't hurt it, sir,' the shopkeeper agreed. 'I will do what you ask.'

He and his friends went back to their shops.

———

Time passed. The busy seaport of Obama became a very important town.

One day, a messenger arrived from the capital city, Edo. He brought a message from the Emperor of Japan. The Lord of Obama had to send an important document to Edo. The Emperor wanted the document very quickly.

When he had prepared the document, the lord put it into a document box. He closed the box and he spoke to one of his servants.

'Call my messenger,' he said. 'He must take this docu-ment to Edo immediately. He must arrive there in seven days. It is a long way from here to Edo. My messenger is the only man who can run fast enough.'

The servant left the room but he soon returned.

'Sir, your messenger is very ill,' he said. 'He cannot run to Edo.'

The lord was worried. 'If I do not send the document to Edo, I will fail in my duty,' he thought. 'I will be disgraced. The Emperor will not trust me any more.'

Who could take the document to Edo in seven days? The lord asked his servant to write out a large notice. The notice said:

> **A REWARD**
> **A bag of money to any man**
> **who can run to Edo in seven days**
> *The Lord of Obama*

The servant put the notice on a wall outside the lord's house. That afternoon, a stranger arrived at the lord's house. He was a young man.

'I will take the document to Edo,' he said.

'I do not know you,' said the lord. 'You do not live in Obama.'

'No,' replied the stranger. 'My name is Hachisuke. I am visiting Obama. I saw the notice on the wall.'

'Can you run to Edo in seven days?' asked the lord.

'Yes,' said Hachisuke. 'Nobody can run faster than me.'

The lord had no choice. The emperor had asked for the document. The lord had to send the document to Edo. It was his duty. He gave the document box to the young man.

'Go now!' he said. 'Run as quickly as you can.'

———

The days passed and the Lord of Obama waited. On the seventh day, Hachisuke returned. He had run to Edo and he had returned to Obama in seven days!

The lord was very pleased with Hachisuke. The young

man had saved him from disgrace. 'No messenger can run as fast as you,' he said.

The lord gave the young man a reward – a bag of money.

'Will you stay in Obama, Hachisuke? Will you be my messenger now?' the lord asked.

'I will,' Hachisuke replied.

So when the lord had an urgent message, he called for Hachisuke. The young man always did his work well. He ran faster than any man. The lord liked Hachisuke very much.

'Hachisuke can run as fast as the wind,' he said. 'He is always happy and kind.'

One day, the lord had another important document for the emperor. He called for Hachisuke.

'You must take this document box to Edo,' he said. 'Then you must wait. Bring an answer from the emperor. You must be back in Obama in ten days from now. Go quickly, Hachisuke!'

———

The Lord of Obama waited for Hachisuke to return. But he did not come on the tenth day. The lord was surprised because the young man had never been late before.

'The weather is bad,' the lord thought. 'The rain has made Hachisuke late. He will come soon.'

Day after day, the lord waited for Hachisuke. But the young man did not come. The lord was sad because he liked his messenger very much. He sent some men to look for Hachisuke. They walked all the way to Edo but they did not find the messenger.

A week later, the lord was walking in the forest near Obama. Suddenly, he saw something lying beside the path. It was small and it had red fur. It was a dead fox.

The little animal had been killed by a dog. Its fur was covered with blood. The marks of a dog's teeth were on its body. And there was something in the fox's mouth. The lord looked closely at the fox. In its mouth, the fox held the lord's document box!

The lord was sad. It was the fox which he had rescued from the shopkeepers. At last he understood. The fox was Hachisuke! The lord had saved the fox's life. And the fox had helped him.

The fox had given him a reward. The fox had changed into a man. It had become his messenger, Hachisuke. The fox had saved the lord from disgrace. Hachisuke could run faster than any man because he was a fox! He had changed back into a fox and he had run with the lord's messages. He had run with the lord's document box in his mouth.

But a fox cannot run faster than a dog. And when a dog had attacked him, Hachisuke could not fight the dog. He could not fight it because he did not want to drop the lord's document box.

Sadly and slowly, the lord walked back to Obama. He carried the little body of the fox. He went into his garden and he dug a hole in the ground. And he buried the fox in the hole.

Then the Lord of Obama made a shrine. He made the shrine for Inari, the god of foxes. And he made the shrine for his messenger, Hachisuke.

He made the shrine for Inari, the god of foxes.

THE STORY OF HOICHI'S EARS

1

The Battle of Shimonoseki

Shimonoseki is a city on the coast of Japan. It is at the western end of Honshu Island. There is an old Buddhist temple in Shimonoseki. The temple is by the sea. Many years ago, this temple was the home of a musician called Hoichi.

Hoichi lived at the temple all his life. He had a little house and a garden. They were in the big garden of the temple. The monks were his friends and they took care of him. They took care of him because Hoichi could not see – he was blind. He was blind when he was born. But he became a wonderful singer and a wonderful player of the *biwa*.

Many of Hoichi's songs were about the history of Japan. They were very old songs. They were about famous men and famous battles. The most famous song was about the Battle of Shimonoseki.

When he was an old man, Hoichi had many visitors. He was often asked about the Battle of Shimonoseki. And he often told the story.

'Hundreds of years ago,' said Hoichi, 'there were two great families in this part of Japan – the Heike family and the Minamoto family. The Heike people and the Minamoto people hated each other. They fought each other for many years. And they fought their last battle here at Shimonoseki. It was a great battle on the sea. The Minamoto people won the battle. All the Heike soldiers were drowned. They died in the sea. And all the Heike women were killed.

'There was a very young Heike prince,' Hoichi went on. 'A young woman was taking care of him. She was his nurse. The nurse saw the Heike soldiers drowning. She saw the Minamoto winning the battle. She was very frightened. So she put the young prince into a boat. She tried to escape with him. But they could not escape from the Minamoto. The nurse held the little prince in her arms and she jumped into the sea. The nurse and the prince were drowned.

'For many years after the battle,' Hoichi continued, 'the coast and the sea near this place were haunted. The spirits of the Heike people were not at peace. The people who lived in Shimonoseki were afraid. On dark nights, when there was no moon, they looked at the sea. They saw thousands of small lights above the water. The lights were the spirits of the Heike.

'Many swimmers in the sea were suddenly pulled under the water,' said Hoichi. 'Many swimmers were drowned. The people of Shimonoseki stopped swimming in the sea.

'Everybody wanted the spirits of the Heike to be peaceful,' said Hoichi. 'They wanted the spirits to stop haunting the coast. So this temple was built. And a cemetery was made for the dead Heike people. The people of Shimonoseki put stone monuments in the cemetery. These monuments were to the Heike soldiers. On the monuments, they wrote the names of the soldiers who had drowned. There was also a monument for the little prince. Now, Buddhist monks in the temple pray for the dead people. And at last, the spirits are peaceful.'

Hoichi did not tell the visitors everything about the Heike spirits. But he often sang the song about the Battle of Shimonoseki. He sang it on warm summer evenings. He sat outside his little house in the temple garden. And all the monks and visitors listened. When he sang that song, everybody was quiet. When Hoichi sang about the little prince and the nurse, many people had tears in their eyes.

2

Hoichi Sings

Hoichi learnt the song about the Battle of Shimonoseki when he was a young man. And soon many people came to hear him sing it.

'That young man, Hoichi, sings that song better than anybody,' said the abbot of the temple. 'Soon, he will be a famous musician.'

The abbot – the most important monk in the temple – was a wise man. And he was Hoichi's friend. Every evening, he came to Hoichi's little house and talked with him for an hour.

One summer morning, the abbot spoke to the blind musician.

'I will not visit you this evening, Hoichi,' the abbot said. 'I must go to another temple for two days. I will visit you when I return.'

That evening, Hoichi sat outside his house. Hoichi's house had a small garden. The ground was covered with many kinds of stones. It was very quiet in the garden.

It was very hot and Hoichi did not want to go inside. He did not want to go to bed. Soon it was very late and very dark. But Hoichi still sat outside his door.

He picked up his biwa and touched the strings gently. Then he began to sing:

Hoichi played his biwa and he sang.

Once there was a great sea battle,
Near this town, Shimonoseki.
Many Heike soldiers died here,
Many frightened women cried here —

Suddenly, Hoichi stopped singing. He heard some footsteps. Somebody was walking over the stones of his small garden.

'Who is it?' Hoichi said to himself. 'It is not the abbot. He is not in the temple.'

The footsteps stopped near him. He heard a deep voice. 'Hoichi! Hoichi!'

'Who are you?' Hoichi asked. 'I do not know your voice. What do you want?'

'Do not be afraid, Hoichi,' said the voice. 'My master sent me to you. He is a great lord. He is visiting Shimonoseki. He wants to see the famous place where the battle was fought – the last battle of the Heike and the Minamoto. Many other lords and ladies are with him.

'My master was told about you, Hoichi,' the voice went on. 'He was told about your singing and playing. He wants to hear your song about the Battle of Shimonoseki. Bring your biwa. Come with me!'

It was very late and Hoichi was tired. But a poor man cannot disobey a lord. Hoichi stood up.

'Sir,' he said. 'I am blind. You must lead me to your master.'

A strong hand held Hoichi's arm and led him out of the temple. He was led through the streets of the town.

After a long time, Hoichi heard the deep voice again. 'Open the door!' it said. 'Hoichi has come.'

Hoichi heard a door open. Then a soft hand held his arm and he was led through many rooms. Hoichi smelled sweet perfume.

'A great lady is leading me,' Hoichi thought. 'I can hear the sound of her silk dress. And I can smell her sweet perfume.'

Soon, Hoichi heard the voices of many women. The women were all around him. They were whispering.

'Please sit down here, Hoichi,' said a lovely soft voice. 'Please sing the song about the Battle of Shimonoseki.'

Hoichi sat down on a soft cushion. He started to play the biwa gently. And then he sang:

Once there was a great sea battle,
Near this town, Shimonoseki.
Many Heike soldiers died here,
Many frightened women cried here —

The song was very long. Hoichi sang beautifully. And he played his biwa wonderfully. His strong fingers moved quickly over the strings. Sometimes the sound of the biwa was like the waves of the sea. Sometimes it was like the noise of the battle. Sometimes it was like the sound of many women crying.

Hoichi sang about the Heike lords who were drowned. He sang about the Heike ladies, crying for their men. And he sang about the deaths of the women and the children.

At first, there was silence all around Hoichi. But then he sang about the little prince and his nurse. Hoichi heard many women crying.

At last, the blind musician finished his song. He heard again the soft voice speaking. It was the lady who had led him into the room.

'My master is very pleased with you, Hoichi,' she said. 'He wants you to sing again tomorrow night. We will stay here in Shimonoseki for six days. You must come each night and sing for my master. You must sing about the Battle of Shimonoseki.

'The man who brought you here will take you home,' the woman went on. 'He will bring you here again tomorrow night. But do not tell anybody about your visit to us. If you come here every night, and if you do not tell anybody, my master will give you a good reward.'

Again, the soft hand held Hoichi's arm. He was led to the door. Again, he heard the deep voice of the man who had brought him from the temple.

'Come, Hoichi,' he said. 'I will take you home.'

———

The next night, the same things happened again. It was very late when the man with the deep voice came to Hoichi's house. Again, he led Hoichi through the streets. Again, the lady with the lovely voice led Hoichi to a room where there were many people. Again, Hoichi sang his song about the Battle of Shimonoseki. And again, the man with the deep voice led him back to the temple.

3

The Words of the Lord Buddha

The next day, the abbot returned to the temple at Shimonoseki. Immediately, he walked to Hoichi's little house. He spoke to the blind musician.

'How are you? Hoichi,' he asked. 'What have you been doing?'

For a moment, Hoichi did not speak. Then he said, 'I am well, my friend. I have been sitting in my house. I have not left the temple.'

The abbot was a very wise man. He was worried.

'Hoichi is not telling the truth,' he thought. 'He is ill. Someone has put a spell on him.'

The abbot left Hoichi's house. He called two young monks. He spoke to them quietly.

'Please watch Hoichi carefully,' he said to them. 'Please follow him when he leaves the temple. I am very worried about him. Somebody has put a spell on Hoichi. Our friend is in danger!'

All that day, the two young monks sat near Hoichi's house. Evening came and soon it was dark. It started to rain, but Hoichi came out of his house and sat in his garden. He gently played his biwa.

At midnight, Hoichi stood up. He held out his right hand and he walked out of his garden. He walked out of the temple garden and through the streets of the town.

The two young monks started to follow him. But it was very dark in the town. Soon, the young monks could not see Hoichi. They looked in all the places where the blind musician liked to sit. They could not find him.

'We must go back to the temple,' one of the monks said. 'We must tell the abbot about Hoichi.'

'Yes,' said the other monk. 'Let's walk through the cemetery. That is the quickest way to the temple.'

But when the monks walked into the cemetery, they heard Hoichi's voice. He was singing the song about the Battle of Shimonoseki. The monks soon found the blind man. He was sitting in front of the monument to the little Heike prince. He was singing and playing his biwa. The rain was falling on him and he was very wet. But all around him, little lights were moving up and down.

Quickly, the monks took Hoichi back to the temple.

The next day, the abbot spoke to the blind musician.

'The spirits of the dead Heike people have put a spell on you, Hoichi,' he said.

'I did not know where I was. I did not feel the rain,' Hoichi replied. 'I was inside a great house. I was singing to lords and ladies.'

'The spirits have power over you, my friend,' said the abbot. 'You are in great danger. Each time you go with the spirits, a part of you will stay in their world. Soon you will disappear from our world. You must not go to the cemetery again.'

'The spirit with the deep voice leads me there,' said

Hoichi. 'I have no choice!'

Then the abbot had an idea. He told Hoichi to take off his robe.

The abbot took a brush and some ink. He wrote all over Hoichi's body. He wrote holy, powerful words. Soon, Hoichi's body was covered with words about the Lord Buddha. There were words on Hoichi's head and on his hands and on his feet. There were words on his chest and on his back.

'The spirits will not be able to see you now,' said the abbot. 'When the spirit with the deep voice comes for you, you must not move or speak. He will not know where you are.'

At midnight, Hoichi was sitting outside his house. He heard the deep voice.

'Hoichi! Come! The lords and ladies are waiting for you.'

Hoichi did not speak and he did not move.

'Hoichi! Where are you?' the voice said.

Still Hoichi did not speak or move.

'He has gone,' said the voice. 'But he has left his biwa and his ears here. I will take those. Then my master will not say, "You have failed in your duty." He will not punish me.'

When he heard these words, Hoichi remembered something. The abbot had forgotten to write any holy words on his ears. The spirit could see his ears!

Suddenly, Hoichi felt a terrible pain. His ears were torn from his head. But he did not move. And he did not make

*Soon, Hoichi's body was covered with words about the
Lord Buddha.*

a noise. He heard the spirit pick up the biwa and walk away.

———

For many days, Hoichi was very ill. The abbot called a doctor. The doctor washed the wounds on Hoichi's head. The abbot prayed to the Lord Buddha.

Hoichi had no ears, but he lived until he was very old. He became a famous musician. Often, he sang the song about the Battle of Shimonoseki. When he sang that song, he remembered the spirits. He remembered the night when his ears were torn from his head. But the spirits never came to the temple again.

THE FARMER AND THE CRANE

1

The Sad Farmer

Every autumn, cranes arrive in Japan. In the summer, these beautiful birds live in other countries. They live in the northern lands. But every winter, the cranes live in the rice fields of Japan. Japanese farmers love to see these graceful birds. 'The cranes will bring good luck,' they say.

One autumn evening, long ago, a young farmer was walking home to his house. He had worked all day in his rice fields and he was tired and hungry. He was also sad. He was sad because he was alone. His mother and father were dead. He could not ask a woman to marry him because he was poor.

'There will be nobody in my house to greet me,' he said to himself. 'I will eat my meal alone. Then I will go to sleep.'

The farmer looked around him. It was nearly dark but it was a lovely evening. In the evening light, the farmer saw many cranes flying across the sky.

He walked quickly. He wanted to get to his house before it was dark. Suddenly he heard a soft, sad cry.

'Someone or something is in pain,' he thought. 'Someone or something is calling for help.'

The farmer stopped and listened.

'Was that a cry of a man or an animal?' the farmer asked himself. 'Or was it the sound of the wind?'

He heard the cry again. Yes, it was a cry for help. It came from the other side of the fields.

'What is it?' the farmer asked himself again.

The farmer was a kind man. He turned round and he walked across the rice fields. Soon he had the answer to his question. He found a beautiful white crane. One of her long legs was caught in a trap.

The farmers always put traps in their rice fields. There were many rats in the fields. The rats ate the rice, so the farmers tried to catch them. They put the traps in the fields to catch rats.

But this trap had caught a crane. The strings of the trap were around her leg. She was struggling but she could not get out of the trap.

'Poor bird, I will help you,' the farmer said softly. He quickly cut the strings of the trap. 'Fly away now,' he said.

But the crane was very tired. She had struggled for a long time. Now she was too tired to fly.

'Poor bird,' the farmer said again. 'I will take you home. I will give you some food and I will wash your leg. When you are strong again, you will fly away.'

So the farmer carried the bird into his little house. He gave her some of the rice from his own meal. He washed her leg and he put a piece of cloth around it.

A few days later, the crane's leg was better. The young farmer carried the bird outside his house. He touched her beautiful, soft feathers. 'Go now,' he said.

He found a beautiful white crane. One of her legs was caught in a trap.

The crane gave a happy cry and she flew up into the blue sky.

2

The Lady in White

Time passed and the winter came. One evening, the farmer was sitting alone in his little house. Outside, snow was falling. White snow covered the fields. The farmer was eating some rice and some fried beancurd.

Suddenly, there was a knock on the door.

'Who is that?' the farmer asked himself. 'Who is outside in this bad weather?'

Quickly, he got up and he went to the door.

When he opened the door, the farmer saw a lovely young woman. She was dressed in a white robe with a red and black pattern. She was wearing a white scarf over her head. She looked at the farmer and smiled.

'Oh, sir,' she said. 'I am lost. It is so cold and dark. Can I come into your house?'

'Please come in, dear lady,' said the farmer. 'I am a poor man and I cannot give you much. But I will give you what I have.'

The farmer gave the young lady some rice and some beancurd. Then they both drank some hot tea. Later, the farmer gave the young lady some cushions.

'Please sleep on these,' he said.

The next morning, the snow was still falling. The farmer spoke to the young lady.

'You cannot travel today,' he said. 'The weather is too bad. Please stay here until the snow stops falling.'

'Yes,' said the young lady. 'I will stay until the snow stops falling. You are very kind.'

A week later, the weather was still bad. The farmer went to his fields every day. The young lady worked in the farmer's house every day. The farmer was pleased to see her every evening. Soon, he fell in love with her.

One evening, the farmer said, 'Tell me about your life.'

'My mother and father are dead,' the young lady said. 'I am going to the great city to look for work.'

'You could stay here with me,' the farmer said. He was surprised at his own words, but he continued to speak. 'You could stay here and marry me. Please be my wife. I do not have very much now, but I will work hard.'

The farmer was a kind man. The girl liked him very much.

'I will marry you,' she said.

3

The Beautiful Cloth

Next to the kitchen in the young farmer's house, there was a small room. In this room, there was a weaving loom. One evening, the farmer told his new wife about the loom.

The farmer was pleased to see her every evening.
Soon he fell in love with her.

'That was my mother's loom,' the farmer said. 'My mother made cloth with the loom. She used some of the cloth to make clothes for the family. And she sold some of the cloth at the market in the village. When I see that loom, I think of my dear mother. I will never sell the loom.'

The farmer's wife looked at the loom. There was some white thread in a basket next to the loom. The farmer's wife smiled. Then she went into the kitchen to get her husband's evening meal.

The young farmer and his new wife lived together very happily. Each day, the farmer went to work in his fields. Each day, his young wife worked in the house.

———

Winter passed and spring came. One evening, the farmer came home from his fields. His wife gave him a long piece of cloth. It was very beautiful and it was very soft.

'I made this cloth on your mother's loom,' she said. 'I made it today. I used the thread from the basket.'

'You weave very well, dear wife,' the farmer said. 'It is beautiful cloth. And you weave very quickly.'

'Take the cloth to the market tomorrow, husband,' the young wife said. 'Sell the cloth. Use the money to buy some more white thread. Then I will weave some more cloth.'

So the next day, the young farmer went to the village. He sold the cloth in the market. He got a lot of money for the cloth. And he bought a lot of new white thread.

After that, the farmer's wife made cloth every day.

Every evening, when the farmer came back from his fields, there was a new piece of cloth. Many people wanted to buy the cloth because it was so soft. Many people spoke to the farmer.

'Will your wife weave some cloth for me?' they asked.

Soon, the farmer and his wife had a lot of money. The farmer was happy. His wife was beautiful. She cooked wonderful meals for him. She made beautiful cloth which he sold. And they had food for the winter.

The farmer bought his wife some pretty combs for her hair. He bought pretty things for the house. He loved his wife very much.

'Do not weave every day, dear wife,' he said. 'When you are tired, you must rest.'

———

One day in the summer, the farmer was at the market. He went to speak to a shopkeeper who had bought some of his wife's cloth.

'I will bring you another piece of cloth next week,' he said.

'Listen, my friend!' said the shopkeeper. 'We can sell your wife's cloth in the city. People will give us more money for it in the city. I am going to the city next week. You can come with me. Ask your wife to make ten pieces of cloth. We will sell them all. You will be rich!'

The young farmer was excited and happy. He had never been to the great city. He wanted to see it. He wanted to be rich.

That evening, he told his wife about the shopkeeper.

'Will you weave ten pieces of cloth for me?' he asked her. 'If you can weave ten pieces in one week, we will be rich.'

'My dear husband,' his wife replied. 'I cannot weave ten pieces of cloth in one week. I must rest sometimes.' She spoke sadly. 'Why do we need so much money?' she asked. 'Aren't you happy now?'

'Yes, I am happy,' said the farmer. 'But I want to go to the great city. And I want to buy some pretty jewellery for you.'

The farmer's wife loved her husband very much. 'I will try to weave ten pieces of cloth,' she said. 'I will try to do it for you.'

———

The next morning, the farmer's wife started weaving. She worked all day. She did not stop working. The loom made a loud noise – CLACKETY-CLACK. CLACKETY-CLACK.

In the evening, she showed her husband the cloth which she had made.

'It is very beautiful and very soft, dear wife,' he said.

The days passed. Each day, the farmer's wife worked at her loom. Each evening, she showed her husband some more cloth. But each day, she was thinner. And each evening, she was sadder.

The farmer was excited. He was thinking about the great city. He did not see his wife's sadness.

On the sixth evening, the farmer said, 'I will go the great city tomorrow. Have you made ten pieces of cloth?'

'My husband, I have made nine pieces,' she replied. 'I cannot finish the tenth piece. I am too tired.'

The farmer was sad. And because his wife loved him very much, she was sad too.

'Go to bed now,' she said to him. 'I will work through the night. But you must not come into the small room. You must not see me weaving!'

The farmer went to bed. But he could not sleep. He could hear the loud noise of the loom. CLACKETY-CLACK. CLACKETY-CLACK.

After two hours, he got out of bed. He went to the door of the small room. He opened the door.

He did not see his wife. There was a white crane sitting at the loom. The crane was moving her wings and she was weaving cloth on the loom. Sometimes, she pulled a feather from her body and used it in the weaving.

The farmer understood. His wife was the crane! She was the crane which he had rescued from the trap. She had changed into a woman and she had become his wife. But she changed back into a crane when she made her cloth. She used her own feathers in the cloth. That was why the cloth was so soft. And that was why she had asked him not to come into the room.

The farmer cried out. The crane turned round.

'Now you know what I am,' she said sadly. 'Now I must leave you. I love you very much, but now I must go.'

The crane left the house. With a sad cry, she opened her wings and flew up into the dark sky. She never came back.

There was a white crane sitting at the loom.

THE GOBLIN'S HEAD

There was once a fighting man – a *samurai* – called Kwai Ryo. He was strong and brave and he was a wonderful fighter. He could fight with a sword. And he could fight with his hands. He fought many times for the lord of his territory.

But when his lord died, Kwai Ryo became a Buddhist monk. He cut off his hair and he gave away his money. He travelled all over Japan, and he taught people the words of the Lord Buddha. Kwai Ryo was a good man and he helped many people.

Sometimes, when he was alone, Kwai Ryo practised fighting. He remembered his life as a samurai. If there was danger, he could protect himself and he could protect other people. He was not afraid of men. And he was not afraid of spirits.

———

One day, Kwai Ryo was travelling through a forest in the mountains. There were no roads. There were no houses. It was getting dark, and Kwai Ryo wanted to sleep.

'I will find a place where I can make a fire,' he thought. 'Then I will have a meal and I will go to sleep.'

Kwai Ryo soon found a place where he could sleep. There was some soft grass near a tree. He made a little fire and he cooked a meal. Then he lay down to sleep.

Suddenly, a man walked towards him. The man held a large axe in his hand – an axe for cutting trees.

'I greet you, Master,' the man said. 'Sir, I am a poor

woodcutter. I work in this forest. Sir, it is very dangerous to sleep here in the forest.'

Kwai Ryo laughed.

'Nobody will attack me, my friend,' he said. 'I am a monk. Nobody can steal anything from me because I have nothing. I pray to the Lord Buddha. He will protect me. And I can fight. I am strong and I am not afraid of any man.'

'You are a brave man, Master,' said the woodcutter. 'But there are spirits in this forest. They attack anybody who is sleeping here. They are goblins – wicked spirits who eat men and women. Sir, my home is not far from this place. Please come and sleep there tonight.'

'Thank you, my friend,' said Kwai Ryo. 'You are kind. I will come to your house and I will pray there. The Lord Buddha will protect you and your family.'

Kwai Ryo got up and he went with the woodcutter. They walked through the forest and soon they came to a small house. The house was next to a small stream. The water from the stream fell into a very deep ravine – a wide opening in the rocky ground.

Kwai Ryo and the woodcutter went into the house. There were two rooms in the house, a large room and a much smaller one.

In the large room of the woodcutter's house, four people were sitting near a small fire. There were two men and two women. They got up and they greeted Kwai Ryo.

'This monk will sleep in our house tonight,' said the woodcutter. 'He will be safe from the evil goblins here.'

The house was next to a small stream. The water from the stream fell into a very deep ravine.

One of the women made some hot tea and gave it to Kwai Ryo. Then the woodcutter took the monk into the smaller room. There was a small bed in the room.

'Please sleep here, sir,' the woodcutter said. 'We will all sleep in the large room.'

Kwai Ryo closed the door of his room. But he did not go to sleep. He opened the window and he looked out. It was a beautiful night. The light of the moon was shining on the little house. The noise of the small stream was soft and peaceful. Kwai Ryo started to pray to the Lord Buddha. He prayed for two hours.

When he had finished praying, Kwai Ryo was thirsty. The monk wanted to drink some water from the stream. He opened the door of his small room and went into the large room. Suddenly, he stopped.

On the floor of the large room were five bodies. They were the bodies of the woodcutter and his family. But the bodies had no heads!

'These people have been killed by wicked men,' Kwai Ryo said to himself. 'Their heads have been cut off. The woodcutter was right. This forest is a very dangerous place. I prayed to the Lord Buddha. But I did not bring peace to this house.'

Then he looked again. There was no blood! Kwai Ryo had been in many battles. When people's heads were cut off, there was a lot of blood.

'No!' he thought. 'These bodies are not dead. They were never alive. They are not people. They are goblins!'

Then Kwai Ryo remembered a temple where he had

On the floor of the room were five bodies.
But the bodies had no heads!

stayed. The abbot of the temple had told Kwai Ryo about goblins who ate people. The heads of these goblins could fly away from their bodies. The heads could attack people and kill them!

'The goblins in this house wanted to eat me,' thought Kwai Ryo. 'They were going to kill me, but the Lord Buddha protected me.'

Then Kwai Ryo remembered something else. The old abbot had said, 'You can destroy these goblins. If their heads cannot find their bodies, they lose their power. You must wait until the heads fly away. Then you must hide the bodies. You must hide the bodies in a place where the heads cannot find them again.'

So Kwai Ryo picked up the body of the woodcutter. The monk left the house and he quickly walked to the ravine. He threw the body of the woodcutter into the ravine.

Soon, Kwai Ryo heard voices. He hid behind a tree. The flying heads of the five goblins had returned to the house. They were horrible. Their mouths were wide open. There was blood on their teeth. One of the women's heads flew inside the house. A moment later it came out again, screaming.

'The monk has gone!' the head cried out. 'He has taken the body of our master. We must kill the monk.'

Then, one of the other heads saw Kwai Ryo. 'There he is! Kill him!' it screamed.

The monk was not afraid. He had been a samurai! Quickly, he prayed to the Lord Buddha. Then he pulled a

The monk was not afraid. He had been a samurai!

small tree out of the ground. He ran towards the heads.

The monk hit the heads with the tree, again and again. Four of the heads quickly flew away. But the head of the woodcutter flew towards Kwai Ryo. It tried to bite him with its horrible sharp teeth. It flew round and round Kwai Ryo and it screamed. But it was losing its power. It did not know where its body was. Its teeth bit the monk's robe. But soon the head fell to the ground. Kwai Ryo had destroyed it.

The monk picked up the goblin's head. He held its long hair and he went into the house. The other four goblins had joined their heads to their bodies. But when they saw Kwai Ryo holding their master's head, they ran into the forest. They ran away, screaming and crying. They were never seen again.

Kwai Ryo went outside and buried the woodcutter's head in the ground. Then he said some holy, powerful words and he went back inside the house. The monk lay down on the bed in the small room and he went to sleep. He slept peacefully. The next morning, Kwai Ryo travelled on to the nearest town.

THE WISE MOTHER

1

The Cruel Law

This story is about a Japanese lord and a cruel law. The lord lived hundreds of years ago. At that time, Japan had many lords. All the lords had to do duty to the Emperor of Japan. The emperor lived in Edo. There were many small territories in Japan. Each territory belonged to a great family. But each territory was ruled by its own lord. And each territory had its own laws. Often, the families who ruled the territories fought each other. They wanted to rule their neighbours' territories.

Long ago, the lord of a small territory on Kyushu Island made a new law. The territory was poor and the land was not good. There were many mountains in the territory. It was difficult to grow crops. It was difficult to grow enough food for everybody.

The lord of this small territory was called Tadahide. And he was very worried. When there was not enough food for everybody, he made the new law.

'Anybody who is too old to work must die,' he said.

Lord Tadahide was not a bad man. But his own parents were dead. He had no elderly relations.

The young people of the territory were very unhappy. They respected elderly people. The elderly people could not work. But they were wiser than their children. They could give their children good advice. The young people loved their parents and their elderly relations. They did not want them to die. They wanted to take care of the elderly people. But nobody could disobey the lord.

When a man or a woman was sixty years old, they had to die. Their children had to take them to a mountain and leave them there. The mountain was called Old People's Mountain. All the people of the territory were sad when they thought about Old People's Mountain, but they had to obey the law.

And soon there was another new law.

'Anybody who has an elderly relation in their house will be killed too,' said Tadahide.

———

In a village in Tadahide's territory, there lived a young farmer. He worked very hard in his fields and he took care of his mother. His father was dead. The mother and son were poor, but they were happy. The young farmer loved his mother very much.

One evening, the farmer came home from his fields.

His mother gave him a bowl of rice and beancurd.

'My son,' she said, 'this is our last meal together. Tomorrow, I will be sixty years old. Tomorrow, you must take me to the Old People's Mountain.'

The young farmer was very sad. 'Mother,' he said, 'I do not want you to die. I will put you in a secret place in the house. Nobody will know. I will take care of you.'

'No, my son,' said the old woman. 'Somebody will tell

the lord. Then you will be killed. I will go to the mountain tomorrow and I will die there.'

The next morning, the young farmer and his mother left the village. They walked slowly towards Old People's Mountain. When the old woman was too tired to walk, the young man carried her. He carried her on his back. At last they reached the mountain.

They came to a place where the grass was soft. The birds were singing. There was a small stream making a peaceful sound.

'Put me down now,' the old woman said. 'I will stay here. This is a beautiful place. This is a good place to die. Goodbye, my son. I hope you will find a good wife one day. She will look after you and love you. Do not forget your old mother.'

The young farmer could not say anything. He turned and walked away. He was crying. Sometimes he turned and looked back at his mother. She waved her hand at him.

'Goodbye!' she called.

The young farmer walked towards his village. He tried to forget about his mother but he could not forget!

'Soon it will be dark,' he thought. 'My mother will be alone in the dark.'

Suddenly, he stopped. He turned round and he started to walk back towards the mountain. He quickly found his mother. He did not say anything. He picked her up and he carried her back to the village.

When they reached the village, it was dark. Nobody saw them. The young farmer carried the old woman into the house. He carried her down some stairs into a cellar. He put a bed in the cellar and he brought his mother some food.

The next morning, the young man went out into the village. He spoke to his neighbours.

'My mother was sixty years old yesterday,' he said. 'I

took her to the mountain.' And he cried.

The months passed. Every evening, the young farmer went down into the cellar. He took some food and drink to his mother and they talked for an hour.

One evening the young man said, 'I will always take care of you, Mother.'

'You are a good son,' the old woman replied. 'I am happy here. But I want to see the sunlight again.'

'One day, you will see the sunlight again, Mother,' said the young man.

2

Good Advice

Lord Tadahide sat in his beautiful large house. He was worried. Lord Tadahide had received a letter. The letter came from the lord of a larger territory. This neighbour's territory was in the north of Kyushu Island. The lord was rich and strong and he had a large and powerful army.

There was bad news in the letter. The lord of the northern territory wanted a gift. If he did not get the gift, his army would attack Tadahide's territory.

Tadahide called his advisers. They were wise men. They gave him their advice when he was worried.

'What shall I do?' Tadahide asked the advisers.

'What gift does the northern lord want?' one of the advisers asked.

'He wants a rope made of ashes!' replied Tadahide.

Tadahide and his advisers thought and thought. But nobody could make a rope from ashes.

'Send a messenger to all the villages,' Tadahide said. 'If any man can make a rope from ashes, I will give him a good reward.'

———

That evening, the young farmer told his mother about the lord's messenger.

'How can anybody make a rope of ashes, Mother?' asked the young man.

'My son, that is not difficult,' the old woman replied. 'You must get a rope. And you must get a bucket of water. Put some salt in the water. Make the rope into a coil and put it into the bucket. Later, take the coil of rope out of the water and dry it in the sun. When it is dry, you can put the coil of rope on a piece of wood and burn the rope. When it has burnt, there will be a rope of ashes on the piece of wood.'

The young farmer listened to his mother. The next day, he made a rope of ashes.

The young farmer took the rope of ashes to Lord Tadahide's house. He gave the rope of ashes to Lord Tadahide.

The lord was very pleased. He gave the young man some money.

————

A few weeks later, Lord Tadahide received another letter from the lord of the northern territory. There was also a long piece of bamboo and a long piece of thread. The piece of bamboo had many bends in it.

Tadahide called his advisers again.

'We must put the thread through the middle of the bamboo,' said Tadahide. 'We must put the thread through the bamboo. Then we must send it back to the northern lord. If we do not send it back in a week, he will attack us.'

The advisers thought and thought. But nobody could put the thread through the bamboo.

Again, Tadahide sent a messenger to the villages in his territory.

'The lord will give a good reward to anybody who can put the thread through the bamboo,' the messenger said.

————

That evening, the young farmer told his wise mother about the messenger's words.

'That is not difficult,' said the old woman. 'Go to the lord's house and ask for the piece of bamboo and the thread. Then you must find a large ant. Tie the thread to the ant. Then put some sugar in the hole at one end of the bamboo. Put the ant in the hole at the other end.

'The ant will walk through the bamboo to get to the sugar at the other end,' the old wise woman went on. 'The ant will take the thread with it.'

The next day, the young farmer went to Lord Tadahide's house. He asked for the bamboo and the thread. He remembered his mother's words. Soon, the thread was through the bamboo!

The Lord Tadahide was very pleased. Again, he gave the young man some money.

A few weeks later, Tadahide had a third letter from the northern lord. The lord wanted another gift. Tadahide called his advisers again.

'The northern lord wants me to send him a drum,' said Tadahide. 'He wants a drum which plays itself. If I send him this gift, he will not attack us. And he will never ask for anything else.'

But none of the advisers could make a drum which played itself. So Tadahide sent his messenger to the villages once again.

That evening, the young farmer went down to the cellar of his house. He spoke to his mother.

'How can I make a drum which plays itself?' he asked.

'That is not difficult,' his mother replied. 'You must find a drum. Then, take off one end of the drum and put some bees inside it. Then, put the end back on the drum. The insects will fly against the ends of the drum. The drum will make a noise.'

So the next morning, the young farmer found a drum. He put some bees inside it and he took it to Lord Tadahide's house. Lord Tadahide was very pleased. He sent the drum to the northern lord. Then he spoke to the young farmer.

'You have saved our territory,' Tadahide said. 'Now, we shall not be attacked. What reward do you want?' he asked. 'Do you want some more money? Or do you want something else?'

'My Lord,' answered the young farmer. 'I will ask for a reward which is not money. I want you to change a law. In this territory, all people who are sixty years old must die. That is the law. Elderly people cannot work in the fields. But they are wise. Elderly people can give us good advice.

'I made the rope of ashes,' the young farmer continued. 'I made the drum which plays itself. I put the thread through the bamboo. But my mother told me what to do. She is old but she is very wise. I did not save our territory, my Lord. My mother saved our territory.'

Lord Tadahide understood. 'It is a cruel law,' he said. 'I will change it.'

That afternoon, the young farmer went home. And he led his mother out of the cellar. He led her into the sunlight.

Points for Understanding

THE LORD OF OBAMA'S MESSENGER

1 What was Obama? Where was it?
2 Describe the Lord of Obama.
3 What things were sold in the market?
4 Who shouted and ran? Why?
5 The lord spoke to a man. What did he ask the man? What answer did the man give?
6 The messenger could not run to Edo. Why?
7 Why was the lord worried?
8 The Lord of Obama was going to give a reward.
    (a) What was the reward?
    (b) Who was going to get the reward?
9 Who was the stranger? What question did the lord ask? What was the answer?
10 The stranger was going to take a document box to Edo and wait for an answer. When did he have to return to Obama?
11 The messenger was late. What did the Lord of Obama think?
12 What was beside the path in the forest?
13 What did the Lord of Obama build in his garden?

THE STORY OF HOICHI'S EARS

1

1 Where did Hoichi live?
2 Who took care of him? Why?
3 What was Hoichi and what did he do?
4 The Heike people and the Minamoto people hated each other. What happened?

5 Why were the people of Shimonoseki afraid?
6 What did the people of Shimonoseki build near the sea?

2

1 One night it was very hot. Hoichi did not want to go to
   bed. What did he do?
2 What happened next?
3 Hoichi was led through many rooms. 'A great lady is
   leading me,' Hoichi thought.

3

1 What did the abbot think?
2 Two young monks followed Hoichi.
   (a) What did they see?
   (b) What did Hoichi do?
3 What did the abbot do to Hoichi?
4 What happened at midnight?
5 What had the abbot forgotten to do?
6 What happened to Hoichi?

THE FARMER AND THE CRANE

1

1 Which birds arrive in Japan in the autumn?
2 Why do the farmers like to see them?
3 Why was the young farmer sad?
4 The young farmer heard a soft, sad cry.
   Who or what did he think it was?
5 How did the young farmer get the crane out of the trap?
6 What did the young farmer do next?

1 Who came to the farmer's house when the snow fell?
2 Describe this person.
3 'I am a poor man and I cannot give you much,' said the farmer.
   What did the farmer give to his visitor?
4 'Tell me about your life,' the farmer said.
   What did the visitor tell him?
5 What did the farmer ask the visitor? What did the visitor reply?

1 Where was the loom?
2 Who had used the loom before?
3 One evening, the farmer's wife gave him a long piece of cloth. Where had it come from?
4 Where did the farmer take the cloth?
5 The shopkeeper had an idea. What was his idea?
6 What did the farmer ask his wife to do?
7 Why did he want her to do this?
8 The days passed and the farmer's wife worked at her loom. Describe the farmer's wife now.
9 The farmer could not sleep. Why?
10 The farmer went into the small room.
   (a) What did he see?
   (b) What did the farmer understand now?
   (c) What happened next?

THE GOBLIN'S HEAD

1 Kwai Ryo had been a samurai. What was a samurai?
   What did Kwai Ryo do?
2 What happened when his lord died?

3 Kwai Ryo met a woodcutter. What was he carrying?
   What did this man do?
4 What did the woodcutter tell Kwai Ryo? What was
   Kwai Ryo's reply?
5 What are goblins?
6 Describe the woodcutter's house.
7 Kwai Ryo did not go to sleep immediately. What did he
   do?
8 What did Kwai Ryo see on the floor of the large room?
   What did he think?
9 Kwai Ryo remembered an old abbot's story. What was the
   story? What did Kwai Ryo think then?
10 What did Kwai Ryo do with the body of the woodcutter?
11 What did the goblins do?
12 How did Kwai Ryo fight the goblins?
13 What did the woodcutter goblin do?
14 The other goblins ran away. Why?

THE WISE MOTHER

1

1 What was the name of the lord of the small territory on
   Kyushu Island?
2 Why did he make a new law?
3 What was the new law?
4 Why were the young people unhappy?
5 Where did sixty year old men and women have to go?
6 What was the other new law?
7 How did the young man take his mother to Old People's
   Mountain?
8 What did the young man think when he walked towards
   the village?
9 What did the young man do?
10 What did he say and do when he saw his neighbours?

1 Lord Tadahide received a letter.
  (a) Who was it from?
  (b) What did this person want?
  (c) What was going to happen?
2 What gift did the northern lord want?
3 The young farmer asked his mother about the lord's message. What was her answer?
4 What happened when the young man went to see Tadahide?
5 The northern lord sent a second letter to Tadahide. What was with the letter?
6 What did Tadahide and his men have to do?
7 The messenger went again to all the villages. The young man told his wise mother the messenger's words. What instructions did she give to her son?
8 What happened when the young man followed these instructions?
9 Tadahide had a third letter. What did the northern lord want next?
10 What did the wise mother say when she heard this news?
11 Tadahide wanted to give the young man another reward. What did the young man ask for?

ELEMENTARY LEVEL

A Christmas Carol *by Charles Dickens*
Riders of the Purple Sage *by Zane Grey*
The Canterville Ghost and Other Stories *by Oscar Wilde*
Lady Portia's Revenge and Other Stories *by David Evans*
The Picture of Dorian Gray *by Oscar Wilde*
Treasure Island *by Robert Louis Stevenson*
Road to Nowhere *by John Milne*
The Black Cat *by John Milne*
The Red Pony *by John Steinbeck*
The Stranger *by Norman Whitney*
Tales of Horror *by Bram Stoker*
Frankenstein *by Mary Shelley*
Silver Blaze and Other Stories *by Sir Arthur Conan Doyle*
Tales of Ten Worlds *by Arthur C. Clarke*
The Boy Who Was Afraid *by Armstrong Sperry*
Room 13 and Other Ghost Stories *by M.R. James*
The Narrow Path *by Francis Selormey*
The Lord of Obama's Messenger and Other Stories
by Marguerite Siek
Why Ducks Sleep on One Leg and Other Stories *by Anne Ingram*
The Gift From the Gods and Other Stories *by Anne Ingram*
The Land of Morning Calm and Other Stories *by Anne Ingram*
Love Conquers Death and Other Stories *by Catherine Khoo and Marguerite Siek*
The Stone Lion and Other Stories *by Claire Breckon*
The Bride of Prince Mudan and Other Stories *by Celine C. Hu*

For further information on the full selection of Readers at all five levels in the series, please refer to the Heinemann Readers catalogue.

Macmillan Heinemann English Language Teaching, Oxford

A division of Macmillan Publishers Limited

Companies and representatives throught the world

ISBN 0 435 27324 8

Heinemann is a registered trademark of Reed Educational & Professional Publishing Limited

The stories *The Courier of the Lord of Obama*,
The Farmer and the Crane, *The Goblin Head*,
The Ears of Hoichi and *The Old Mother* were first published
by Heinemann Southeast Asia
(a member of the Reed Elsevier plc group)
in **The Golden Legends of Japan** by Marguerite Siek (1996)
© Marguerite Siek 1996

These retold versions by F.H. Cornish for Heinemann Guided Readers
Text © Reed Educational and Professional Publishing Limited 1997
Design and illustration
© Reed Educational and Professional Publishing Limited 1997
First published 1997

Illustrated by Lisa Jensen
Illustrations and map, pages 5 and 6, by John Gilkes
Typography by Sue Vaudin
Cover by Yukki Yaura and Marketplace Design
Typeset in 11.5/14.5pt Goudy
Printed and bound in Great Britain by Fine Print (Services) Ltd., Oxford

97 98 99 00 10 9 8 7 6 5 4 3 2 1